Doin Mi Ed In

David Orme lives in Winches[...] wide variety of poetry text books and picture books for young children. He is the editor of the Schools' Poetry Review and spends a great deal of his time in schools performing and writing poetry, and encouraging children and teachers to take an active interest in poetry.

Martin Glynn is one of Britain's best known exponents of contemporary forms of the African oral tradition. He also spends much of his time in schools working with children and developing their writing skills.

Also in this series:

'ERE WE GO!
Football poems
chosen by David Orme

DOIN MI ED IN

Rap poems
chosen by David Orme
and Martin Glynn

Illustrated by Jane Eccles

PIPER
PAN MACMILLAN
CHILDREN'S BOOKS

First published 1993 by
Pan Macmillan Children's Books
a division of Pan Macmillan Publishers Limited
Cavaye Place London SW10 9PG
and Basingstoke

Associated companies throughout the world

ISBN 0 330 32817 4

9 8 7 6 5 4 3 2 1

A CIP catalogue record for this book is available from
the British Library

Photoypeset by Intype, London
Printed by Cox & Wyman

'Passing' by Lucy Pyne (page 46) was an award-winning entry in the 1991
WH Smith Young Writers' Competition.

Contents

Introduction

You might think you know what is meant by rap and dub poetry, but how much do you know about their history?

Rap and dub are based on the African oral tradition, but this tradition has been reshaped, reworked, and given a new name.

Griots can still be found in Africa. These are men and women who keep history alive in a village or district. They are highly respected by some and feared by others! Griots use music, drama, poetry, dance and song to present their stories. Sometimes the wholy history of an area, going back hundreds of years, can be brought to life by a Griot.

As the African peoples became spread throughout the world by migration and slavery, new ways of practising the old traditions emerged. Important amongst these are the development of Gospel, Blues, Jazz-Poetry, Soul/Funk, and so on. Each one of these musical art forms has contributed to rap.

Caribbean traditions have followed that route of development, using accentuated rhythms coupled with beats, to create different styles. Each island has its own rich blend of word forms and music.

Jamaica has always had a history of folk historians, who would sing about Jamaican life. This was called Mento. Out of this came the great tradition of reggae disc jockeys, storytelling to reggae music. This was positive and creative, but something else was needed – something that would reflect Jamaica's turbulent history using the language of struggle. This led to dub poetry, which developed by using the rhythm and beats of a reggae dub (drum and bass instrument) but using the voice as the main instrument.

The important thing about rap and dub is that they are meant to be heard. Dub performers use a strong dialect: look at 'Bes Fren' on page 56. But reading the poems in this book cannot capture the essence of a live performance, so:

Perform them!

Go out and listen to rap and dub performers!

Go to the library and read material about African/American and Black British poetry.

Write one to perform yourself, for you are the new innovators and guardians of the oral tradition.

How to Write Dub and Rap Poetry

One Choose a subject, for example, **POETRY**.

Two Write down as many words as you can that are connected with your subject:

> **POETRY RHYME RHYTHM**
> **FUN HARD EASY**

Three Find words that sound alike and pair them up:

> **PO ET RY**
> **EA SY**

Four Now try to put sentences in front of the words that rhyme, to tell a story. Your rap has got to make sense!

> I really enjoy writing **PO ET RY**
> It's **EA SY**

Five Next add some more lines. Remember, you will be reading it out loud, so show how clever you are in arranging the words rhythmically!

> I'm clever with words
> Enjoy writing **PO ET RY**
> I'm a cool type of person
> It aint hard it's **EA SY**

Here's a dub version:

> Mi clever wid
> **WURDZ**
> Mi enjoy writin
> **POETREE**
> Mi cool as a breeze
> It nuh hard
> It easy

9

Six Experiment with your own ideas. Put the sentences and words into a different order. If you can get hold of a metronome, a keyboard, or even a clock, you'll be able to get a greater variety of beats and rhythms, which will help you compose a wide range of styles to assist you in creating ideas.

Seven Once you have composed your piece and perfected it, you have to PERFORM IT!

Before You Perform Your Rap . . .

- Learn it! This doesn't mean you have to present it without a script. It just means that you have to have the confidence to use the script only as something to fall back on. Although most people who perform rap and dub poetry do learn it by heart, having the words with you on paper gives you confidence – and that's **crucial!** If you can learn your rap it will leave you free to do other things since you won't be holding pieces of paper. It can also be quite distracting for an audience to see bits of paper being waved about! If you perform as a small group, you could learn a bit each, then come together with a chorus line – like the 'Baby Rap!' on page 18.

- To learn it, either read it to yourself a line at a time or record it onto a cassette player or video. Listen to it a number of times, until you start to remember it.

- Once you have learnt it, try **performing** it in several different ways until you find the one that you are happy with. Because it is a performance, you will find it never sounds the same twice, although some things, like the meaning, will remain the same.

- It is important to understand the **emotion** of your rap, so that you can convey this to an audience. It would be silly to write a poem about death, then read it in a funny voice (unless that is the effect you want to get over).

- Try your piece out on friends, who will give you constructive criticism to help build your confidence.

- After a few times performing to friends or family, you should be ready for a wider audience. As you grow in confidence you will find it easier to play and experiment with different styles.

- Go to it! Be a performer!

Everybody Rap

Can you do a rap?
      Can you do a rap?
Can you make a rhyme?
      Can you make a rhyme?
Can you link up words,
      Can you link up words,
To help me blow my mind?
      To help me blow my mind?

    Poetry is the thing that we can do
    To show that there's no difference
    Between me and you.

Black and white are all the same
And those who say different are mad insane.

    Do you agree?
    I said do you agree?
    If you agree,
    Say yowl to me.

Su Andi

Hats for Cats

I was walking down the road on my way to school
When I met these cats playing the fool.
They were dancing on the pavement, spinning on their backs
And all of them were wearing hats.

They were singing a song which sounded like a rap
And the song they sang was HATS FOR CATS!
HATS FOR CATS MAN HATS FOR CATS!
And the song they sang was HATS FOR CATS!
I stood on the corner listening to the rap
When they saw me there in my old school cap.
They said, 'Join in the fun boy, join in the fun,
This singing and a'ringing has just begun.'
We were popping and a'bopping all the way to school
Everyone we passed thought us real cool.
The headmaster was standing in his cap and gown
When he saw us coming he gave us a frown.
But he listened to us, then joined in,
You should have seen him doing that spin!
The teachers and the children they had a ball
Moon-walking in the Assembly hall.
The song we sang was HATS FOR CATS!
HATS FOR CATS MAN HATS FOR CATS!

The BBC heard about us
We went on TV and caused quite a fuss.
The news media they came around
And everybody joined in the sound.

Soon the nation was a'singing as they joined in the beat
Even Mr Major found his feet.
We went to the Palace and Charles and Di
Were spinning and a'popping till they got quite high.
My friend Tabby he looked at the Queen
He said, 'Queenie Queenie, where have you been?'
She looked back at him – put on her crown,
Then she began spinning around.
She said – 'WAVE!'
We said – 'WAVE!'
HATS FOR CATS MAN HATS FOR CATS!
The name of the song is HATS FOR CATS!
Various nations sent their spies,
They could hardly believe their eyes.
News got around that the world was a'spinning
Everybody in the world was a'dancing and a'singing.
We sang PEACE!
We sang LOVE!
HATS FOR CATS MAN HATS FOR CATS!
Everybody sing HATS FOR CATS!

Christine Michael

Machoman

I ain't no SCHWARZENEGGER
Or a CLAUDE VAN DAMME
Ain't a BRONSON or a RAMBO
Or a ROBOCOP man
I don't have ripplin biceps
An oozi or a nine
Or plant the seeds of bad behaviour
Firmly in my mind
Don't like the virtue of obsession
Pickin on the weak
Although I'm wise, and know what's happenin
Down there on the street
I don't like people walkin round
Thinkin drugs are cool
When CRACK, COCAINE and HEROIN
Is just a game fer fools
An attitude of mind I hate
I see so much, it's SLACK
When access is denied to me
Because my skin is BLACK
I see them in the ghetto streets
Actin out the violence
That takes away the breath of life
Leaving blood and silence
Too many times, we stand and watch
Observe and stand and stare
Because we just don't give a damn
An option not to care
Alarms that deafen all our ears
Can never stop the thief
The tears I see, and cries I hear
The anguish and the grief
Of those whose loved ones snatched away

Hear the screams and moans
Of victims of the joyrider
The crunch of broken bones
I cry inside with deep despair
Which quickly turns to rage
When the target for a mugger
Is defenceless, and elders age
I watch those eager to prove themselves
Following the trail
Leading to the space in hell
Your own apartment, JAIL
So smile away, behave so bad
Put malice in your head
Being macho ain't a virtue
When prematurely dead

Martin Glynn

17

Baby Rap!

Adults go gooey with a baby on their lap,
it's the cootchy-coo, cuddly-poo baby rap.

> Woopsy, poopsy, honey bun,
> sweetie, tweetie, sugar plum,
> snuggums, diddums, cutesie tootsie,
> bunnikins, honeykins, footsie wootsie.

Out on the street adults push their buggies,
desperate for coos and lots of huggies.
When baby cries; time to change that nap,
parents smile for it's their time to rap!

Woopsy, poopsy, honey bun,
sweetie, tweetie, sugar plum,
snuggums, diddums, cutesie tootsie,
bunnikins, honeykins, footsie wootsie.

Adults enjoy being a patter chatterbox
with 'precious, izzums, bless your cotton socks.'
So when babies cry, 'daddeeee, mummeeee,'
all adults do is shove in a dummy!

Woopsy, poopsy, honey bun,
sweetie, tweetie, sugar plum,
snuggums, diddums, cutesie tootsie,
bunnikins, honeykins, footsie wootsie.

Babies must wonder what's happening here,
all this cooey talk dribbling in their ear.
Those adults so noisy and full of prattle
perhaps their mouths should be stuffed with a RATTLE!

Woopsy, poopsy, honey bun,
sweetie, tweetie, sugar plum,
snuggums, diddums, cutesie tootsie,
bunnikins, honeykins, footsie wootsie.

Adults go gooey with a baby on their lap,
it's the cootchy-coo, cuddly-poo baby rap!

Ian Souter

The Money Blues

I was sitting in my room
The other day,
When I looked in my purse
Then started to say,
'I got the no money blues . . . What am I gonna do?'

I started looking round
In case there could be
Some money just waiting there,
Hiding from me –
I got the no money blues . . . What am I gonna do?

I went to my mum,
Who barely looked down on me,
But managed, 'You see I have a money tree.'
I went to my dad,
Who started to say,
'When I win the pools . . .'
This was not my best day.

Our neighbour, she passed by
And I gave her a smile
When she asked if I'd
Look after her child for a while.
I got the no money blues ... What else could I do?

I told her, this time
I couldn't do it for free.
She said she understood,
And had meant to pay me.
I got the no money blues ... What else could I do?

She told me the hours,
I told her my rate,
She quickly cut the time,
'I won't be out that late.'
I went to her home,
Her child reached for me,
My day was looking brighter
When he said, 'I'm sleepy.'

I was feeling real good
So I called up my friend.
He said he'd meet me later,
Does this day have to end?
I got the some money glee ... I'm so glad to be me.

I chose something special,
We went somewhere to eat –
The Wimpy tasted great,
I made it my treat.
I got the some money glee ... I'm so glad to be me.

Then someone I knew
Made me truly turn red,
Hailed me out in public.
'Did you hear what I said?
Where's my money you owe?'
She shouted at me;
The shekels in my purse
Were in her hands so quickly!

My bus fares to my house
Was all that remained.
Yes, home was my retreat –
I'd been too badly shamed!
I had the some money glee . . . It departed from me.

Money was the root
Of my problem that day.
I learned my lesson well,
Though it'd been the hard way.
I had the some money glee . . . It departed from me.

Now when I have some money
I include in my plans
To pay back my dues
As soon as I can.
Sometime it could prove
To be the key
About keeping a friend
Or getting an enemy.

My parents aren't surprised
When I volunteer
To do some extra housework –
Many chores they prepare.
I got the no money blues . . . But I know what to do.

So I earn my pocket money,
Now I know how to spend
And save the odd penny,
I'll reach there in the end.
I got the no money blues . . . But I know what to do.

Amelia Wade

Rap-Pin

Now am a poeter –
An am a real cool dude.
Some om me poems are clean
But some of them are rude.
An I come to you from a place called Speke.
Where you have to be tough!
You get nottin if you're weak.

Well other guys call me Terry an it ain't no jest
When it comes to being a poeter you're looking at the best
When it comes to rapping
Am a rapper too
When it comes to break dancing am the cat for you!
Cat for you
Cat for you
Cat Balou (meow)

Am cool am slick am all too much, but
There's even one thing that I won't touch –
An I ain't slow
An I ain't no slouch
Don't give yer earache and I ain't no grouch
But if you're hanging around like a soap on a rope
One thing yer don't mess with is glue or dope
'Cos it messes up your life and gives you such a cough
Take a whiff or have a sniff (and) watch your head roll off
Head roll off,
Head roll off (ouch!)

So rap with me and have no doubt
'Cos if you mess around with drugs then it'll
F. F. F. F. F.
Fade you out.
Fade you out.
Fade you out.

Terry Caffrey

Yucky Things

Jus like a magician
Performin a trick
The object of this RAP
Iz ter make yer sick
Ter make yer feel bad
Turn yer inside out
Ter put yer head in the sink
Make yer stomach shout out
Wearin my tracksuit
Sittin on my bum
Realised I woz sittin
On chewin gum
It woz glued to my bottom
Whether I liked it or not
But it couldn't compare
To blowin some . . . . . SNOT
Out of my nose, there it goes
So I took a big bogey
Wiped it on my clothes
There it woz, on my shoulder
A bogey ball, as big
As a boulder
Takin off my socks
My face didn't grin
I had em on fer two weeks
They were full of dead skin
Now, I ain't sophisticated
An I ain't posh
But my runny sweaty armpits
Just needed a wash
So I put in the water
Picked up the soap
Hadn't washed fer weeks
My body couldn't cope

Hard skin on my feet
Woz flaky and tuff
It blended in well
With all my dandruff
Went round my fingers
Gave em a suck
Cleaned under my nails
I swallowed the muck
In my nails it tasted stale
A cross between cheese
An eatin a snail
My toothpaste screamed
It woz scared to death
When it caught the smell
Of my awful breath
I woz lookin kinda good
I woz feelin really neat
So I went to the kitchen
Decided to eat
My smile disappeared
I forgot I woz mean
The bread that I had
Woz mouldy an green
I wasn't upset
As I heard my brain mutter
So I left the bread
An ate some butter
Put the oil in the pan

This woz no joke
Eatin an egg
With a stone cold yolk
Placed it on the green bread
With some greasy cold chips
Bit thru the yolk
It ran down my lips
Now I needed a drink
Ter bring my stomach
Ter the boil
So I drank a custard skin
With cod liver oil
Put my dirty clothes on
Made my way outside
Then something bad happened
I cried an cried
There woz a pigeon on the ground
Layin there dead!
Coz it just dropped a message
Over my head
It woz then I woke up
It woz all in a dream
I looked at my body
I woz smelly but clean
So I woz jus like a magician
Performin a trick
I hope the rap makes yer
WANNA BE SICK!
UGH!!!!!!!!!!

Martin Glynn

Thirteens doin mi ed in

At thirteen
Everyfings doin yu ed in
Schoolz
Doin mi ed in
Home works
Doin mi ed in
Teachez
Are doin mi ed in
Momz
Doin mi ed in
Dadz
Doin mi ed in
Auntys, uncles
Are doin mi ed in
Baby bruvvers
Definitely
Doin mi ed in
Money problems
Doin mi ed in
Cant have a mountain bike
Thats doin mi ed in
Mom says take a hike
Doin mi ed in
Mi girlfrenz
Doin mi ed in
Mi mates
Are doin mi ed in
Cant wait
Till Im eighteen
Cause thirteens
DOIN MI ED IN

Yvonne Mitto

Give Me the Strength

Give me the strength
to scrub out the dirt
to iron the shirt
to massage the hurt
to hoover the floor
wipe the marks off the door
to clean the sore finger
that got shut in the door
while I hoovered the floor
give me the strength
to buy some more bread
to straighten the beds
to bandage the head
that got knocked in the shed
while I straightened the bed
give me the strength
to walk to the school
to wait at the gate
to wait while they're late
to hurry them home
to answer the phone
give me the strength
to plaster the cut
the drawer wasn't shut
while I answered the phone
shouldn't be left alone
now the telly is on
and the others have gone
down the street
for some sweets
can I please just have one
MINUTE'S PEACE?

Trevor Millum

Ozone Friendly Poem

It won't damage the EARTH,
or pollute the sea
it won't psych your mind
neither poison your body
these words have power
when used properly.
Because
This poem is OZONE FRIENDLY.

Words can be creative
words can sound great
we can use words to instruct
and to communicate,
these words are not destructive
violating a tree.
Because
This poem is OZONE FRIENDLY.

My words take shape
they are organised
they won't burn the EARTH'S skin
like pesticides
they're not manufactured using CFCs.
Because
This poem is OZONE FRIENDLY.

Digest these words
feel positive
don't panic, get stressed
they're free from additives,
you won't regurgitate them
like smoke from a factory.
Because
This poem is OZONE FRIENDLY.

These words are SAFE
I can testify
they won't destroy the OZONE LAYER
beyond the sky,
you can analyse this poem
in a laboratory.
You'll find
This poem is OZONE FRIENDLY.

Recycle, regenerate
don't waste energy
conservation of the EARTH
is just a part of the key

and I'll keep on using these words
well naturally.
You see
This poem is OZONE FRIENDLY.

Levi Tafari

I Lost My Voice

Did I lose my voice
        on an InterCity train?
Or is it soaking through the soil
        with the pouring rain?
I lost my voice,
        and I don't know where to look,
Perhaps I pressed it flat
        between the pages of a book?

Did I lose my voice
        on a busy street corner?
Maybe it's drowning
        in a bottle of Kia-Ora,
I lost my voice,
        and I'm short on words,
Maybe I forgot myself
        and fed it to the birds?

Did I lose my voice
                    at a supermarket checkout?
Perhaps it slipped from my lips
                    just before the shout?

I lost my voice,
        I've almost given
        up the search,
Maybe someone's found it
        on a pew in
        church?

I lost my voice
            and I want it back,
Is it lurking in the pocket
        Of my plastic mack?
Could it be that butterfly,
        buffeting the breeze?
Perhaps the split second
        just before a sneeze?
I lost my voice
        and I want it ba

Simon Pitt

Music is a Natural High

Play me again 'n' again
Like a video game
Puttin my name
In the audio hall of fame
Don't smoke crack from a pipe
I let turn-tables smoke
An I broke
The mic right extention
My musical invention
Relieves tension
Another dimension
Of leisure, pleasure
You can't measure, the treasure
Endeavour
For release of pressure
My grooves new improved
If ya don't move
Off the wall
You'll be surgically removed
As high as the ASTROIDS
I can dance 24 hours
And don't need steroids or 'Es'
Ecstasies or LSD
Who needs these
Oh! people please
Like a plough
Propelled by a mule
Music's the fuel
'N' ya feet are the tool
Go a cappella, the tempos kept
Accept . . . it's hereditry, ancestry, legacy
Like I'm a guy
'N' birds can fly

Black people can dance
So we don't ask why
I'm in a rave relaxin
'N' see 100 kids out-dance
MICHAEL JACKSON
Like a magical mystery tour
Your sweat will pour
But ya still on the dance floor
Should I stop?
Get outa here!
Does a deep sea fish
Ever come up for air
When I dance I revive those vibes
My ancestors tribes
Did, when they woz alive
Yeah! I'm tellin ya, these moves ya do
They did before you in ALKEBU
You take drugs to dance, but why
When music is a NATURAL HIGH

**Felix Joseph
(Black Radical Mark 2)**

Teenage Meanage

Teenage
Meanage
What an age to be
I wanna be you
And you wanna be me
Fashions
Passions
Things you have to wear
Bright clothes
Right shoes
Then of course the hair
Can't be seen
To be coming off the scene
Might lose my cred
Mom sends me to bed
Teenage
Meanage
What an age to be
So much pressure
Coming from afar
Can't wait to come in late
Have my own car
Go to a bar
Stay out all night
Do things that aren't right
Have money
Jingling in my pocket
Sounds like honey
Teenage
Meanage
What an age to be

Yvonne Mitto

RAPunzel

Not once but
twice upon a time coz ya ain't heard my speak
this ain't no fairy tale   this is reality
live in a tower block   call it hell
but it never get me down my name is RAPunzel

The lift never works an' it smells of piss
I'm tellin' ya sis, it can't go on like this
my auntie says, 'I'm gettin old, I can't make the stair:
RAPunzel   RAPunzel   let down ya hair!'

I tried the weavin   tried the waxin
hot comb curly perm and relaxin
hair meant to grow but nothin hapnin
filled with a dread   that I am a baldhead.

So
she trudge an she trudge an she trudge to meet me
she hum a tune and she read graffiti
she's busy   she's gettin dizzy
I'm so ashamed that my hair is short
and frizzy.

An a man stands   on the ground floor
don't know what he's hangin aroun for
he serenades me   with Public Enemy
he's crazy   or is he?
He seems to like me   I say politely
come up an see me   if you dare
RAPunzel   RAPunzel   LET DOWN YA HAIR

Then I have an idea
I take a trip ta Dalston   then ta Brixton
never have no money for no hair decoration
stay in the underground an rap like hell
I gotta use my head my name is RAPunzel
I need a twenty metre hair extension
thought I'd mention, ain't no pretension
wholesale   retail   strong enough to abseil
gals get plaitin   RAPunzel's rappin

Home   an sittin in my easy chair
RAPunzel   RAPunzel   LET DOWN YA HAIR

Now he climb an he climb an he climb to meet me
he got a brand new rap to treat me
Urgggh he's ugly   but he loves me
looks ain't everything can't see him when he hugs me
I try to tease him   I try to relax him
slot his favourite track in   nothin hapnin
all brawn no brain think I'll axe him
he's borin   I'm yawnin

Next mornin
Auntie   keep hummin that tune
Mr Public Enemy's commin soon
Get out the scissors now he's there
RAPunzel   RAPunzel   LET DOWN YA HAIR

We gather the hair in a great big bundle
liberate Rapunzel   I ain't no damsel
chuck this vanity   throw it out the window
keep my sanity   no good for him though

He's OK   just a bit shaken
think he's got the message if I ain't mistaken
not my type   even though I like
Don't Believe The Hype

I say   Auntie   ya gotta good sensa rhythm
we're gonna win em   us women
get out the ghetto   ain't no lookin
back   you backin   me rappin

She say 'daughter   thought ya'd never ask
we gonna live it happy ever after
pack ya bag   clear ya head   check this sound
ya let down ya hair now ya gonna let ya hair down!'

Twice upon a time check   this women
this ain't the endin it's the beginin
twice upon a time check   this men
does your hair stand   on end?

Patience Agbabi

The Disco Sheep

The disco sheep danced down the street.
He stomped his hooves to a disco bleat.

'I'm Sam the Ram. So form a queue.
I'll dance with ewe and ewe and ewe.

'I'm the best at The Hip Hop Skip.
Your number one at The Sheep Dip Trip.

'All you sheep wherever you are,
Shout Sam the Ram – Superbaah.'

John Coldwell

The First Woman in my Life

A woman's work is never done
if you don't believe me ask my mum
she worked her fingers to the bone
to provide us with a decent home
If she lived in ancient Rome
she could've built that city on her own
she cooks, she cleans
she does everything
she irons, decorates and she does the shopping
She chastised us when we were rude
but never sent us to bed without food
everyday she would change our clothes
if we had colds she would wipe our nose
or if we went to her with a problem
mum would always help us solve them
We didn't want for anything
we got the greatest gift her lovin
You can have ten aunties
and scores of lovers
but remember you only have one mother
I remember someone called me a nigger
mum says you're Black, beautiful and you have a culture
She always made sure we went to school
cause in this life you can't be a fool
you see people will ride you like a mule
it was mum who taught me to be cool
Mother there is something I want you to know
I love you, I love you, I love you so
you taught me to survive in the ghetto
you can have my last ROLO
If it wasn't for you I wouldn't exist
so here it comes for you a kiss
Yes you were the first woman in my life
but one day I will take a wife
then like you she will become a mum
A woman's work is never done.

Levi Tafari

Ghost Town

From the backstreets down by the aqueduct
comes an undead crowd with their blood all sucked.
They've a dreadful smell. They don't look well.
Their souls are sold to him from hell.
They've grown stone-cold and their eyes are glazed.
When they smell warm flesh, they become half-crazed.
They're just like something from a horror movie.
If they weren't so real, they'd be well groovie.

> They're dead, but they won't lie down.
> They're dead, but they won't lie down.
> They're in our town and they're walking round.
> They're dead, but they won't lie down.

Wherever we go, they're in hot pursuit,
So we stab, we shoot, we electrocute
To no avail; though God knows why
they refuse point-blank to properly die.
We can't even go to the supermarket.
They crowd round the car when we try to park it.
The dog got out and can't be found,
Though we can hear it howling underground.

> They're dead, but they won't lie down.
> They're dead, but they won't lie down.
> They're in our town and they're walking round.
> They're dead, but they won't lie down.

Their clothes are lousy, their complexions vile.
They're the walking weird. They're devoid of style.
They're out all night with their clanking chains.
They eat eyeballs whole and they suck out brains.
And we can't now phone cos they've cut the wires.
And they've crashed the car and slashed the tyres.
And we can't relax cos of all the screams.
When we finally sleep, they invade our dreams.

> They're dead, but they won't lie down.
> They're dead, but they won't lie down.
> They're in our town and they're walking round.
> They're dead, but they won't lie down.

There's a demon in the attic. In the cellar there's a ghoul.
And there's something in the bathroom that's decidedly
uncool.
And *you* don't look too good. Are those maggots in your
hair?
And I'm staring in the mirror but . . . my reflection isn't there.

> We're dead, but we won't lie down.
> We're dead, but we won't lie down.
> We're in your town and we're walking round.
> We're dead, but we won't lie down.

Nick Toczek

Passing

My bus pass is my passport;
>   It's just ten minutes' ride,
From Brixton into Dulwich,
>   It is the great divide.

>   No soldiers here, no checkpoints,
>   No great forbidding wall,
>   But manners, language, customs,
>   You have to change them all.

From Palladiums to loafers,
>   And Chipie to Chanel,
Karan, then into Naf Naf,
>   From street-cred into swell.

These kiss like Continentals
    Or shake a manly hand:
These nod a casual greeting
    And too much talk is banned.

    'Wicked', 'safe' and 'well 'ard',
        Or 'fab' and 'brill' and 'great',
    'Really super, darling',
        Or 'it was blindin', mate'.

I think that I'm bilingual,
    I think that I can pass;
But I'm a tourist really,
    And I'm travelling second class.

Envoy

    Would I rather be a 'Ragga' or a 'Jagger'?
        Would I rather be a 'Shazza' or a 'Sloane'?
    I think that all this class
        Is just a load of farce –
    I'd really rather make it on my own.

Lucy Pyne

Tell-tale Rap

Katie Pratt's a scaredy-cat —
wouldn't kiss Chris

    no Chris
        no Chris
            going to tell Miss

wouldn't hold his hand or
let him walk her home.
With Christopher Fitzdribblelip
she wouldn't be alone!

                no Chris
                        no Chris
                                going to tell Miss
                                going to tell
                                going to tell . . .

Katie's in a tizz.

Katie's got her knickers
truly in a twist —
to Christopher Fitzdribblelip
all she'll say is this:

                no Chris
                        no Chris
                                going to tell Miss
                                going to tell
                                going to tell . . .

but how can I resist?
Christopher Fitzdribblelip
I'll see you after six

                but don't tell
                        don't tell
                                don't tell
                                        Miss.

Gina Douthwaite

A Car Called Heapsville

She's a little red Mini
That rattles like a tin
Her tyres are illegal
Cos the rubber's wearing thin
So don't brake too hard
Or you'll send her in a spin

But I'll go a million miles in that car
Cos she's my four wheeled superstar

The steering wheel's loose
There's rust in the sill
But she's a great little mover called
HEAPSVILLE

When you drive away
You leave a heap of dust
But it ain't no dirt
It's a pile of rust
There's corrosion in the wings
And stretch in the springs
There's moths in the seat
And holes by your feet
so you can see the road
passing by a treat
This car's got cool upholstery –

It the only thing that passed
The MOT . . .

But I'll go a million miles in that car
Cos she's my four wheeled superstar

The subframe creaks
But I can't pay the bill
So I just keep on driving that
                    HEAPSVILLE

She never gives up
when you've got a full load
Just dribbles black oil
All over the road
The door comes open when your turning left
But she's insured – third party, fire and theft
I wouldn't swop a limo for my little red banger
Cos she gets rock music on an old coathanger

But I'll go a million miles in that car
Cos she's my four wheeled superstar

She blows out steam
When she's going up a hill
But I just keep on driving that
                    HEAPSVILLE

David Orme

The Swing (Moods of Life)

Oopar Niche . . tu ichko kai
           tu ichko kai

Oopar Niche . . oo ichko kam
           oo ichko kam

      Tu ichko kai
      oo ichko kam

Oopar Niche . . tu ichko kai
Oopar Niche . . oo ichko kam

      Tu ichko kai
      Oo ichko kam
      Oo ichko kam
      Tu ichko kai

Oopar Niche . .
Niche Oopar

      Oo ichko kam
      Oo ichko kam
      Tu ichko kai
      Tu ichko kai

Oopar Niche . . niche oopar
Oopar Niche . . niche oopar

      Oo ichko kam
      Tu ichko kai
      Tu ichko kai
      Tu ichko kai
      Tu ichko kai
        Tu ichko kai
        Tu ichko kai
        Oo ichko kam

Mary D. Chauhan
Poem uses three basic lines: the swinging
motions of a swing. Phonetically written in
the language of Gujerati.

Dub Poetry

I wanted to write some dub poetry,
so I settled to write inna dif'rent stylee.
From quarter to ten, to half past t'ree,
but I couldn't write dub poetry,
so I went off to have a cream tea.

The place I went was like a home from home.
Home made jam, fresh made scones,
all very English, but it's part of me,
why can't I write dub poetry?

Next I went to the library,
but all they had was Keats and Shelley.
Shakespeare was all that was taught to me.
Why can't I write dub poetry?

I went back to write dub poetry,
sure it would come like A, B, C,
but the language of dub is foreign to me.
Because in this country it's hard to keep the language
and culture of your parents alive; which is why I
couldn't get this last line to rhyme properly.

Bertel Martin

Bored

I'm kicking
  a ball
I'm kicking
  a ball
I'm kicking
  a ball against a wall

I'm bored
I'm bored
I'm bored   I'm bored   I'm bored

I'm banging
  my head
I'm banging
  my head
I'm banging
  my head against a wall

Hey!
  there are some girls
Hey!
  there are some girls
Hey!
  look over there (where?)
  there are some girls

I'm dribbling
  the ball
I'm heading
  the ball
I'm bouncing
  the ball back off the wall

I'm cool
I'm cool
I'm cool   I'm cool   I'm cool

Hey!
there go the girls
Hey!
there go the girls
Hey!
there go the girls, the girls have gone

I'm kicking
        a ball
I'm kicking
        a ball
I'm kicking
        a ball against a wall

I'm bored
I'm bored
I'm bored   I'm bored   I'm bored

I'm banging
        my head
I'm banging
        my head
I'm banging
        my head against a wall   **Bernard Young**

Bes Fren

Five an five
A ten
Mi an yuh
A Fren

Noh worry bout dem
Dem cyaan trouble yuh agen

Dem a fool
Dem noh run dis school
Dem a fool
Mek dem gwaan goh kool

Dem noh waan fi
Read an write
Dem ongle waan fi
Fus an fite
Den noh waan fi
Draw an spell
Das why dem get expel

Dem a fool
Dem noh run dis school
Dem a fool
Mek dem gwaan goh kool

Well a gwine tell yuh dis
But a naw tell yuh dat
Mi naw tell yuh nutten
Dutty or slack
mi naw tell yuh
Bout horse dead an cow fat
Anyting mi chat
is a fact.

Dem a fool
Dem noh run dis school
Dem a fool
Mek dem gwaan goh kool.   **Ras Largo**

Rice Pudding

I'm asking the angels in heaven
To listen to my prayer
I'm sure if they heard my reasons
They'd agree it isn't fair.
Now I'm a good girl I am
I work as hard as I play
But as soon as the dinner bell rings
On my knees I pray.

Please no more rice pudding
Please no more of that
It's gooyie horrid lumpy stuff
It makes my tummy fat.
I love rice with curry
And risotto I think is great
I adore rice as a main course
But not on my pudding plate.

I'll eat up my flies graveyard
I'm not afraid of ghosts
But rice pudding is the thing
I hate the most.
It's disgusting revolting
It makes my stomach weak
The thought of it gives me nightmares
I'm losing out on sleep.

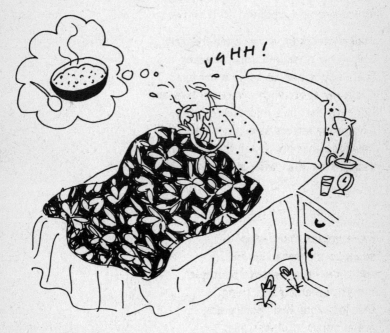

Frogs legs I'll eat them
Snails rolled up in spice
Caterpillars with fur on
Anything but rice
Puddings made from cockroaches
Sprinkled heavily with weeds
But angels please hear me
No more rice pudding please.

Su Andi

I'm Into Techno

I'm into techno
machine mad man
finger on the button
never need to lift a hand
I'm gaga for the gizmos,
like to strike the right pose,
fully-automated, computer-calculated,
future-proofed, updated so it shows . . .

I bake ice-cream in my oven-freezer
I blow my nose in a solar sneezer
I've a robot bed to service my head
I pick my spots with a vacuum tweezer
I dry my hair in a microwave sink
I write my letters in electric ink
my video-mirrors as tall as the wall
with a screen as wide as a skating-rink

If I see a gadget I've got to get it
to pet it or regret it or forget it or set it

I've a greasy micro-chip
stuck to my lower lip
and a twenty megabyte toothpick
I've got an electronic thing
that lets your hear plants sing
green songs in ultra-sonic.

I don't need to think 'cos my bathroom sink
has a brain that knows more than I do,
it can calculate the crumbs
in a dozen current buns
while flushing them down the loo.

I've a burglar alarm with so much charm
that robbers give themselves up
I've a magnetic mouse
that can tidy the house
and a highly intelligent tea cup

I've got machines that dream my dreams
that think my thoughts
that fear my fear
that do my deeds
that scheme my schemes
I've got every machine that there's ever been
and I don't know
why I'm here

Dave Calder

Airmail to a Dictionary

Black is the mellow night
Without the black there would be no white.

Black is the pupil of the sky
Putting colour in the sea's skin and earthen sky.

Black is the oil of the engine
On which this whole world is depending.

Black is light years of space
Holding on its little finger this human race.

Black is the colour of ink
That makes the History books we print.

Black is the army. Wars in the night
Putting on the black to hide the white.

Black is the colour of coal
Giving work to the miners and warmth to the cold.

Black is the strip upon my cardcash
That lets me get money from the Halifax.

Black is the shade of the tree
Sharp in definition against inequality.

Black is the eclipse of the sun
Displaying its power to everyone.

Black is the ink from a history
That shall redefine the dictionary.

Black on black is black is black is
Strong as asphalt and tarmac is.

Black is a word that I love to see
Black is that, yeah, black is me.

Lemn Sissay

'Ere We Go!

Football poems compiled by David Orme,
with football facts by Ian Blackman,
and illustrations by Marc Vyvan-Jones.
Piper £2.99

Football Mad

Gizza go of yer footie,
Just one belt of the ball?
Lend yer me scarf on Satdee
for just one boot at the wall?

Give yer a poster of Gazza
for one tiny kick with me right?
Do y' after be that mingey?
Go on, don't be tight!

A chest-it-down to me left foot,
a touch, a header, a dribble?
A shot between the goalie's legs,
a pass right down the middle?

Y' can borree me Madonna records
for as long as ever y' like,
I'll give yer a go around the block
on me brandnew mountain bike.

One day I'll be playin' for Liverpule
Wen yooze are all forgot:
go on, a titchy kick of yer footie,
one meezly penulty shot?

I'll get yer a season ticket
when I am in THE TEAM,
and wen I'm scorin' in the Cup
you'll be sittin' by the Queen.

Matt Simpson

David Orme is back! With a fabulous collection of poems all
about the one thing guaranteed to interest 99 per cent of
normal human beings . . . FOOTBALL!